Foreword by 1996 Formula One World
Damon Hill OBE

Jim Bamber has a gift for helping us seeing the funny side of what can, at times, be a very unfunny sport. Unless you have experienced the emotional roller coaster of our sport, you will probably be a bit bemused by some of it. But to those of us who have the sport in our veins, Jim's cartoons remind us that it is always better to laugh than cry. It's only a game after all!

Happy laughs

The Prologue

For the last fifteen years I have put all my cartoons of the year into my series of 'PITS' books. The very first one had its foreword written by Damon's mum Bettie so a big thanks to another hero from the Hill family for writing the words to this new Heroes book.

Before the PITS there was a book called 'Eff One' and before that there were four other books called 'Yumping Yarns' published by my friend Billy Campbell in Belfast. This time round I thought I would put together the best F1 cartoons from the past 25 years before I lose the will to live watching yet another F1 procession or lose all my brain cells, whichever comes first.

This book then features a wide selection of my heroes and not all of them are what you would call loveable. Some are villains and some are clowns and I will let you decide who is what.

My only apology is that there are a lot of Scotsmen in the book and also the Brundell Brothers, but they are right at the back where you would expect them to be and I also seem to have slated Lotus and Honda rather a lot and Button and Piquet and the Germans and the Japanese. Oh yes and Montoya too and Ralf and Bernie and Max. But whatever they are there is one thing that they have all contributed to over such a long time. They have made us laugh and for that we thank them, heroes all.

Jim Bamber

This book was published by Fludes SH Ltd 119 Factory Road, Hinckley, LE10 0DP, England. Printed in China by 1010 Printing International Ltd. Printing in whole or part is forbidden except with prior permission from the publisher so watch it. Copyright Jim Bamber 2008 ISBN 0-9543888-6-0

....and Damon did work at it, winning the World Championship in 1996

There was more chance of Max Mosley getting a Christmas card from Ron Dennis than 'Jackie Villynoove' and the BAR team ever winning a GP.

In 2000 during the German GP at Hockenheim some young chappie ran onto the circuit and almost spoilt David Coulthard's day

5

The very moment in Adelaide 1994 when Damon thought he had won the World Championship only for it to be wiped out by a size ten racing boot.

2007 might have been a troubled year for McLaren but with Alonso and Hamilton at each others throats and a spying scandal to boot, it was great entertainment for the rest of us.

Grown men going round in circles. Isn't this what Formula One is all about?

Of the three teams Jenson has driven for, Williams, Benetton/Renault and BAR/Honda guess which one this was?

The joke that David is using is from the late great Scottish comedian Chic Murray.

10

This was during the 1993 German GP when Damon suffered a puncture near the end of the race while leading. 'Ve ver not amused!'

11

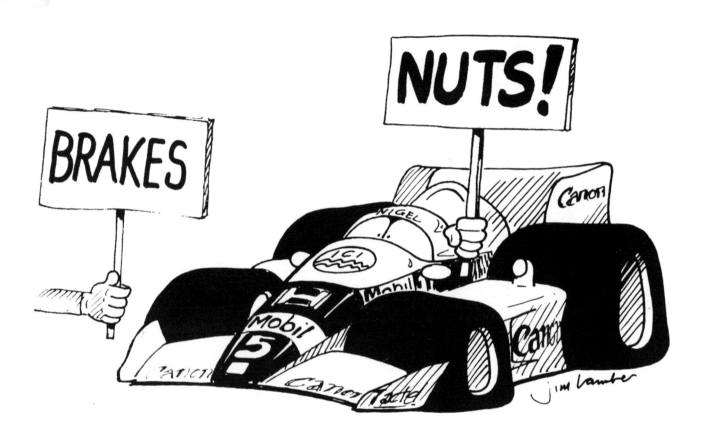

It isn't only the nut behind the wheel who can screw up the race or in this case not screw it up at all. Mansell suffered loose nuts at Portugal 1991 and Monaco in 1992

If I remember this correctly Jenson hurt his back while picking up his wallet during qualifying for a Monaco GP and had to miss the race.

Don't worry, it will all be over by Christmas. The war I mean. The one between the FIA and the F1 teams. I blame it on BMW, they should never have invaded Belgium....or was it Poland?

One year Michael Scumacher won a race when his car was stuck in fifth

15

In 1993 Nigel Mansell went west, met Paul Newman, joined his team and promptly won the American CART championship. Just like that.

This was drawn in 1988 following Ayrton Senna's mysterious crash within sight of his Monaco home. A few years later the original cartoon, signed by Senna, was auctioned for £1800. I had sold it earlier to a 'collector' for £40. Ho hum.

The war between our two heroes continued and I in my best schoolboy German took full advantage. This was Damon taking Michael out at Silverstone.

18

Modern spin informs us that Lewis never said the f-word at all during 2007. We are now told that what he actually said was, 'Dash it all chaps, for the good of my team Vodafone Mercedes McLaren I will be happy to be slower than my very good friend Fernando.'

19

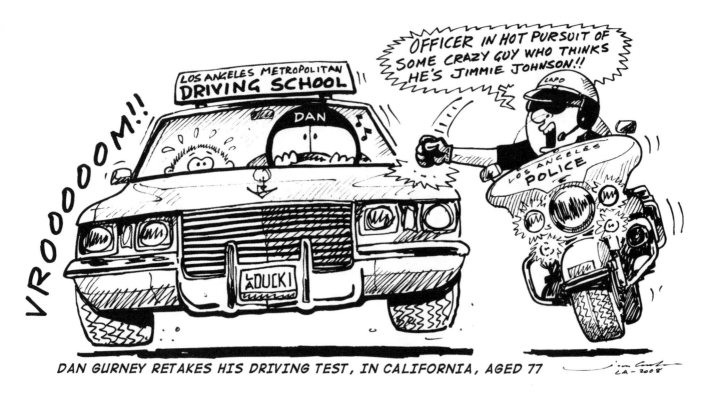

DAN GURNEY RETAKES HIS DRIVING TEST, IN CALIFORNIA, AGED 77

I went to LA in 2008 and met Dan Gurney and yes I have the picture to prove it.
Dan was taking his driving exam that afternoon and I couldn't resist having a pop at
the driver even Jim Clark feared

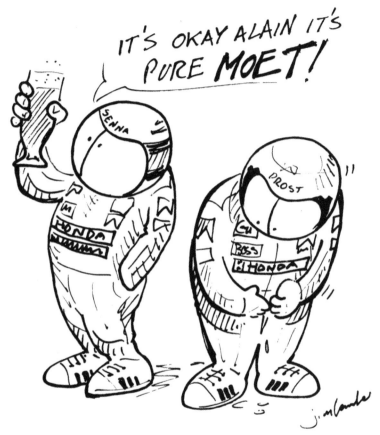

At the 1988 Olympics the fastest man in the world was caught using drugs but for the fastest men in F1, Senna and Prost, winning was the only drug.

Ken Tyrrell was one of the most respected figures in Formula One for nearly four decades but that didn't stop me from having a go at the man who won three world championships.

...and the man who won those three championships with Tyrrell was Jackie Stewart shown here being knighted for his services to the tartan industry.

23

It's 1998 and Michael Schumacher wins the Italian GP but doesn't make the beach in Japan and hands the World Championship to Mika Hakkinen.

One of my all time favourite cartoons featuring, Satoru Nakajima
and Nelson Piquet.

25

Two men who knew how to get the most out of Formula One. Above, Eddie Irvine
in bed with Ferrari....

26

...and Jacques Villeneuve who won a World Championship with Williams in 1997.

THERE ARE ONLY TWO
THINGS BETWEEN ME AND
THE WORLD CHAMPIONSHIP!

YOU AND.....

....THE 'GLEMRINS'

Looks like Mansell has found that loose screw!

Two of my favourite F1 characters, Jean Todt and Ross Brawn of Ferrari doing their best to upset Mika Hakkinen and McLaren.

Just after publishing a book on high performance driving wee Jackie went and crashed a Jaguar sportscar at Silverstone during a test session.

Another favourite character of mine is Frank Williams, here shown rehearsing
a greeting to an old friend. Following the death of Ayrton Senna Williams thought of bringing
back Mansell but in the end recruited David Coulthard.

They are talking about Juan Pablo Montoya who in his time in F1 seemed hell bent on crashing any car he was asked to drive and usually into his teammate.

Two of Formula One's all time favourites, Murray Walker and James Hunt. Their incisive comments didn't always go down well with certain teams.

33

Flavio Briatore now the owner of a football team was years ahead with his rotation policy.

Alain Prost delayed in Monaco by two old women.

Well now you know how Williams came to build a car with the ugliest nose in racing car history.

It's amazing how often racing drivers turn into big babies whenever they don't get their way. In 2007 Alonso was given an FIA minder to hold his hand when he thought that his team didn't love him any more..

The Schumacher brothers, always good for a laugh, especially Ralf who in this case was thinking of leaving F1 for good.

Sometimes a cartoon lands in your lap like at the British GP in 2003 when a man in a kilt ran down Hanger straight. At the same time wee Jackie and the BRDC were getting up Max and Bernie's nose with that old chestnut about saving Silverstone for the nation.

If a team can be a hero then Minardi is the one for me. Run at this time by Paul Stoddart, a well known Australian fork lift driver, the team was a breath of clean air in the paddock.

Senna may have been an artist in a car but 'Our Nige' never gave up.

Yes, he really was that good.

42

In 2007 the relationship between Hamilton and Alonso went from bread to worse.

In all fairness you could probably draw this on the vast majority of racing drivers
who have ever lived!

Montoya could never win against the Schumachers. The odds were stacked against him.

'First floor, lingerie, haberdashery and the World Championship'

Jenson Button, not the best at choosing a team, was denied this particular toy and still drives a Honda

Four hundred years ago these two gents would have been cannonised as Saints. The first is 'Muddly Talker,' otherwise known as Murray Walker....

...and the other is Prof. Syd Watkins who is responsible for the driver's health. In this case checking up on Allan McNish before the Japanese GP in 2002.

49

Prost and Senna playing mind games.

50

What is the latest rich man's toy? A football club of course and they don't come any bigger than.....QPR? The club that Bernie and Flavio eventually bought.

David Beckham and a Spice girl were Bernie's guests at the British GP in 2007.
Victoria! This way Victoria! Give us a smile! Just once! Try!

I was once asked on tv who my favourite driver was and heard myself say that it was Michael Schumacher. I was as surprised as anyone at my own remark but then the man has given me more material than any other living driver.

I don't know why but I've always thought of Team Willy as a crowd of British football hooligans and no better illustrated than when they beat Ferrari way back in 2001.

It's 1989 and Ayrton Senna is on
the beach at Becketts.

During qualifying for the 1988 Hungarian GP, Mansell was a real threat to the McLarens despite suffering from a heavy cold-but come the race he was all wrung out.

I got a thump when Louise Goodman, the ITV commentator, first saw this and I can see I'm going to get another one but there is no denying that she has the finest pair in F1.

This one only really works if you say it out loud.

Shame on me. I stole this idea from the sketch in the 1935 Marx brothers film *A Night At The Opera*.

Every Englishman knows that he cannot pass up any opportunity to take the piss out of our skirt wearing neighbours in the north. I think this was when wee Jackie apeared at Goodwood.

Everybody had high hopes that Michael Andretti would do well in F1 but unlike his dad he couldn't seem to make the transition.

Max and Bernie doing what they do best.

In 1997 team-mate Nakajima was doing quite well in the Lotus, too well for Senna's taste.

In 1988 at Silverstone McLaren were odds on favourites, but nobody had told Mansell.

In another wet race at the 2006 Hungarian GP Jenson Button finally grabbed his first Grand Prix win.

This is Michael and Damon trying to be a little more courteous in their dealings with each other.

In Singapore in 2008 we had the first ever night-time Grand Prix and the surprise winner was Alonso in a Renault thanks in part to the comical antics of Ferrari.

Mansell's second year in America was not as good as his first and he was determined to come home.

In his early years in F1 Jenson Button seemed capable of anything.

These aren't just shorts
they're S&M shorts

Whenever the racings gets dull you can always depend on Max or Bernie to come up with the goods and create some headlines. But even I was taken aback at the lengths Max went to in 2008 to divert attention away from some incredibly boring Grand Prix!!!

At the end of 1988 Mansell announced he was off to Italy to join Ferrari.

Sir Jackie Stewart introducing Allan McNish to the three main contenders for the BRDC chairmanship

1988 was a desert for Lotus.

When the young Mika Hakkinen finally got into a McLaren he outqualified his more illustrious team-mate all too easily.

74

Todt and Brawn making sure that their number two driver knows his place.

Near the end of his F1 career Damon Hill wrote a book which clearly expressed
his views about his fellow drivers

The only outstanding thing about Jenson's 2007 Honda was the colour scheme.

At the first Grand Prix of Bahrain in 2004 Kimi Raikkonen and McLaren seemed to be taken by surprise at the amount of sand in the desert...and in their engines. Doh!

I know, I know, it's silly but I love it.

With a few victories behind him Damon's confidence grew and grew.

Another season, another court case.

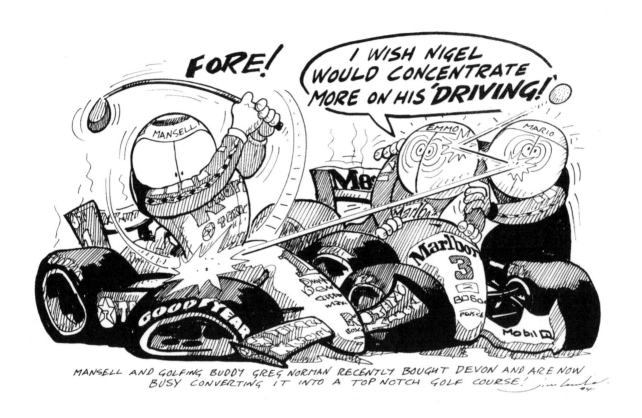

MANSELL AND GOLFING BUDDY GREG NORMAN RECENTLY BOUGHT DEVON AND ARE NOW BUSY CONVERTING IT INTO A TOP NOTCH GOLF COURSE!

At the end of his stay in the USA Mansell seemed more interested in his golfing handicap.

After breaking his leg at Silverstone Michael was determined to get back into his car as soon as possible.

In 1988 Tyrrell had handling problems with their car until they placed a spacer between the chassis and the engine. The lads at Tyrrell paid me to say it was eight inches.

All their hard work was rewarded later in the year when Jenson won the 2006 Hungarian GP.

Things were going from bad to worse at Lotus

In 1995 Michael married his childhood sweetheart Corinna

In 1997 Stewart returned to Formula One to form Stewart Grand Prix, as a team owner in partnership with his son, Paul

When I first drew this it just didn't work until I added Stirling Moss. He loved it.

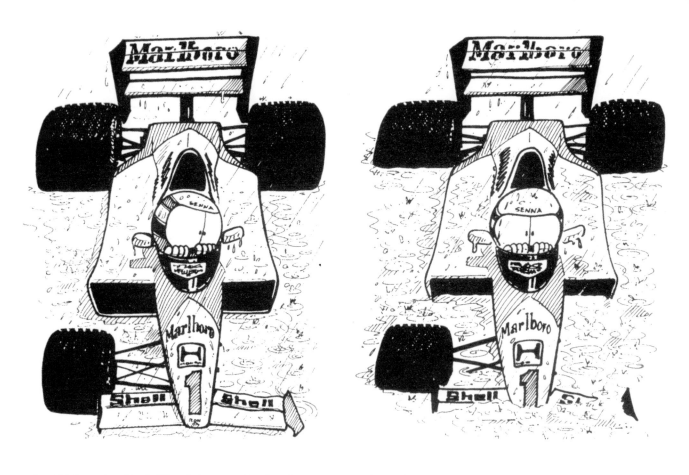

In 1989 at the final GP of the year in Oz, Senna gave his all in the atrocious conditions but....

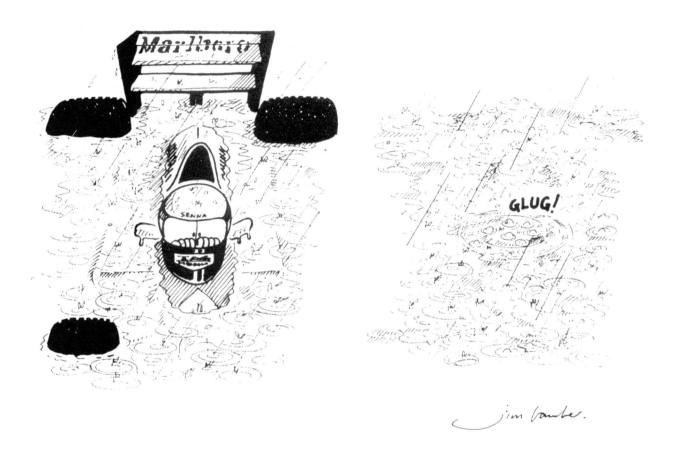

...it was all for nothing as a crash handed the world championship to his rival Prost.

At last! Announcing the famous Brundell Brothers, Mark Blundell and Martin Brundle.
I can't remember if they ever did get to sing the anthem.

I've used this idea a few times too. In this instance it's Nelson Piquet who bore the brunt of my HB pencil. Can you brunt a pencil? Anybody got a pencil sharpener?

You sometimes had the feeling that McLaren didn't always support David in the way they should have.

Draw your own conclusions.

Sub Scribe to and save 20%

Autosport is the World's fastest magazine, bringing you all the new and reviews from F1 to Indycar, NASCAR to LeMans. Don't miss out!

SUBSCRIBE TODAY AND YOU'LL

- Save 20% on the cover price when you pay by Direct Debit
- Pay just £31.20 every 13 issues in easy, manageable instalments
- PLUS get free P&P with every issue!